THE
DAILY SPARK

180 easy-to-use lessons and class activities!

THE DAILY SPARK

Critical Thinking
Critical Writing
Great Books
Journal Writing
Math Word Problems
Poetry
Pre-Algebra
SAT English
Shakespeare
Spanish
Spelling & Grammar
U.S. History
Vocabulary
Writing

THE

DAILY SPARK

Math Word Problems

SPARK PUBLISHING

SPARKNOTES is a registered trademark of SparkNotes LLC.

Spark Publishing
A Division of Barnes & Noble Publishing
120 Fifth Avenue
New York, NY 10011
www.sparknotes.com

ISBN-13: 978-1-4114-9778-2
ISBN-10: 1-4114-9978-6

Please submit changes or report errors to www.sparknotes.com/errors.

Written by Stephen Currie.

Printed and bound in Canada.

Contents

Introduction

The *Daily Spark* series gives teachers an easy way to transform downtime into productive time. The 180 exercises—one for every day of the school year—will each take students five to ten minutes to complete and can be used at the beginning of class, in the few moments before turning to a new subject, or at the end of class. A full answer key in the back of the book provides detailed explanations of each problem.

The exercises in this book may be photocopied and handed out to the class, projected as a transparency, or even read aloud. In addition to class-time use, they can be assigned as homework exercises or extra-credit problems.

Use the *Daily Spark* to prepare your students to tackle the word problems most commonly found on the SAT and the ACT. The *Math Word Problems Daily Spark* gives students lots of practice with standardized-test topics, including exponents and logarithms; money and measurement; number theory; geometry; rates and speed; and ratio, proportion, and percent. *Daily Spark* + Students = Higher Scores!

Spark your students' interest with the *Math Word Problems Daily Spark*!

Building a Box

Tamara builds a wooden box to store mementos from a concert she attended. The length of the box is twice its height and three times its width. If the box has a volume of 36 cubic inches, what is its length in inches?

Squaring the Circle, Circling the Square

For an art project, Laney cuts a circle with a diameter of 6 inches out of a piece of cardboard. Later, she cuts a square with a diagonal of 6 inches out of another piece of cardboard. Which has a greater area, the circle or the square?

A Day at the Beach

After surfing one day, Sam and Pat amuse themselves by drawing acute and obtuse triangles in the sand at the edge of the water. (Geometry comes third in their hearts, after surfing and each other.)

Sam argues that the mean measure of the three angles in an obtuse triangle is greater than the mean measure of the three angles in an acute triangle. Pat claims that the angles in the acute triangle have the greater mean measure. Who's correct? Explain your answer.

Drama at the Photocopier

The perimeter of a certain square is 8 inches. George needs to photocopy the square. He hopes to make a copy that is precisely the same size as the original. However, after making his copy, George discovers that the photocopier is set to magnify whatever he copies by a factor of three—that is, the photocopier triples the length of every line. How many times larger than the original square is the photocopied square?

Maximize This!

What is the greatest number of points at which an ellipse and a rectangle can intersect?

Who Wants to Be a City Planner?

A cybertown is laid out on a grid. The town is in the shape of a square, with the four angles of the square anchored by the homes of the mayor, the town clerk, the prom queen, and the dogcatcher. The mayor's home is at (3, 6) on the grid. The town clerk's home is at (−4, −1). The prom queen's home is at (3, −1). What are the coordinates of the dogcatcher's home?

Qwerty U. Iop

Ayesha's computer keyboard is a rectangle twice as long as it is wide. If the width of the keyboard is represented by k, what is the length of the keyboard's diagonal?

A Four-Sided Figure

The lengths of the sides of a certain quadrilateral are expressed by x, $2x - 3$, $x + 2$, and $3x - 6$. The quadrilateral has a perimeter of 28. What is the length of the quadrilateral's longest side?

Geometry

Coordination

Lynda and Peggy Sue are playing a game on a coordinate grid. Lynda puts a counter on the point (5, 2). Peggy Sue responds by placing a counter on (3, −2). What is the equation of the line made by these two points?

Block Factory, USA

A factory makes wooden blocks that are 4 inches long, 2 inches wide, and 1.5 inches high. These blocks are packed for shipping inside boxes that are 1 foot long, 1 foot wide, and 1 foot high. Assuming they are shaped such that they can completely fill the box, how many of these blocks does it take to fill a box?

Number Theory

Extremely Odd

The sum of five consecutive odd integers is 235. What is the greatest of these integers?

Pitchers, Catchers, and Divisibility

The players on a baseball team each have different numbers on their uniforms. Each uniform number is divisible by two, divisible by three, or divisible by both two and three. Fifteen players have uniform numbers that are divisible by two. Twelve players have uniform numbers that are divisible by three. Six players have uniform numbers that are divisible by both two and three. How many players are on the baseball team?

S, M, L, and XL

A T-shirt stand has 358 shirts in stock in four different sizes: small, medium, large, and extra-large. There are more large shirts than medium shirts, more medium shirts than extra-large shirts, and more extra-large shirts than small shirts. If there are 92 medium shirts, what is the greatest number of small shirts the stand can have in stock?

Remainders Rock

When divided by nine, a certain positive integer k has a remainder of four. What is the remainder when $(2k + 10)$ is divided by nine?

Be There, or Be Square

When an integer x is divided by seven, the remainder is two. When x^2 is divided by seven, what will the remainder be?

Some Sum

Together, three positive integers have a product of 360. The smallest of these integers is 4. What is the greatest possible sum of the three integers?

Number Theory

In Training

During his workout, Sheppard swims 12 laps, then rests for 2 minutes. It takes him 25 seconds to swim one lap. If he swims his first lap at 3:00 P.M. and completes his last lap of the day at 3:40 P.M. that same afternoon, how many laps did he swim in total?

The Imaginary Football League

In the Imaginary Football League, there are two ways to score points. If a team scores a field goal, it gets 4 points. If it scores a touchdown, it gets 9 points. During a game, a team can score field goals, touchdowns, or a combination of each.

- The Dukes score 22 points in a game. What combination of field goals and touchdowns must there have been to reach that total?

- The Meadowlarks score 25 points in a game. What combination of field goals and touchdowns must there have been to reach that total?

- A newspaper headline reports that the Yaks beat the Llamas 23–20. How do you know this headline is incorrect?

Number Theory

You Say Celsius, I Say Fahrenheit

The formula for converting degrees Celsius to degrees Fahrenheit is $F = \frac{9}{5}C + 32$. At which temperature are the Celsius and Fahrenheit readings the same?

Anti-Quarters Zone

Candace has 220 coins. Half of them are pennies. The rest are either nickels or dimes. The total value of the coins is $9.85. How many of the coins are dimes?

Nine-Inch Ribbons

A piece of ribbon is 4 yards long. Jeff cuts the ribbon into x equal pieces, with no ribbon left over. If each piece is 9 inches long, what is the value of x?

The High Cost of Living

It takes a gas pump 4 minutes to dispense 9.5 gallons of gas. If gas costs $2 per gallon, how much will it cost to buy the amount of gas dispensed in 6 minutes?

Money and Measurement

R. Teest's Latest Masterpiece

A wall is 72 inches high and 10 feet long. The brilliant young artist R. Teest paints 16 horizontal stripes on the wall, covering the entire wall. All the stripes have the same dimensions. How many square feet are covered by each stripe?

Got a Pencil?

Yanni buys x boxes of pencils. The total cost of the boxes is d dollars. Each box contains p pencils. Write an expression that gives the cost of one pencil.

Off to Mount Baldy

A hiker can choose either of two water bottles to bring on a hike to Mount Baldy. Bottle A has a base with a radius that is twice that of bottle B, but bottle B is twice as tall as bottle A. Which of the two water bottles has the greater volume, and by how much?

Snack Time

Hugo buys an 8-ounce bag of snack mix. By weight, the snack mix is 35% pretzels, 50% peanuts, and 15% puffed rice. Hugo removes the puffed rice, which he dislikes, and eats all the pretzels and peanuts. How many ounces of food does he eat?

Ratio, Proportion, and Percent

But How Good Is Their Defense?

A basketball team scores on five of every eight possessions—that is, it scores five of every eight times it controls the ball. In a certain game, it does not score on 24 possessions. How many times does the team score in this game?

All Chain and No Saw

Officials at the Acme Chainsaw Company decide to perform a random sampling of 100 chainsaws recently produced at their factory. They discover that six of these chainsaws are defective. Out of every 5000 chainsaws produced in this factory, about how many can the company expect to be defective?

Go Ahead, Make My Software

The ratio of Mac to PC users in the Future Software Engineers of America club is three Mac users for every two PC users. (There are no neutrals in this club.) If there are 75 club members, how many use PCs?

Never Leave Home Without Your Life Vest

Janna and Ashley buy a kayak to use on weekends. Janna pays j dollars and Ashley pays a dollars. Expressed in terms of j and a, what percentage of the total cost of the kayak does Ashley pay?

The Tale of *M* and *N*

m and *n* are positive integers. If *m* is increased by 25% and *n* is decreased by 25%, the two numbers will be equal. What is the ratio of *m* to *n*?

The Gender of Geese in the Gaggle

A gaggle of geese has taken over your school's soccer field. Within the group of geese, there are seven females for every eight males, and there are 16 more males than females. How many geese are there in all?

Ratio, Proportion, and Percent

Three Cheers for Capitalism

Frank buys a commemorative plate for $375, plus 6% sales tax. He pays an additional $6.50 to have the plate shipped to him, but he does not pay sales tax on the shipping charge. Three years later, he sells the plate for 10% more than the total he paid for the plate, including taxes and shipping charges. What is his net profit?

Lights, Camera, Action!

The drama club held several fundraisers to generate money for a new lighting system. Club members took in 36% of what they needed from a bake sale, 20% from a scene-a-thon, and 14% from a car wash. The remaining $750 came from a grant from the local arts council. How much did the lighting system cost?

Ratio, Proportion, and Percent

All Hail to the Yellow, Black, and Green

A square flag includes three colors: yellow, black, and green. The colors of the flag appear in the proportion 3:2:1, with yellow accounting for the greatest area and green accounting for the least. If a total of 48 square inches of the flag is black, what are the dimensions of the flag?

Aromian Southpaws

Exactly 7% of the people in Lower Aromia are left-handed. If there are 2849 left-handed people in Lower Aromia, what is the total population of Lower Aromia?

Fruit Flies and Scientists

In a random sampling of 200 fruit flies in a laboratory, scientists find that 144 flies have normal wings. The rest have wings that are vestigial, or poorly formed. If the lab is home to 2500 fruit flies in all, how many fruit flies would the scientists expect to have vestigial wings, based on the findings from the random sampling?

Don't Forget the Sales Tax

The cost of an ATV is $4500, plus 5% sales tax. Malinda, Ollie, and Greg all chip in to buy the ATV. Greg and Ollie each pay the same amount of money. Malinda provides $\frac{3}{7}$ of the cost. **How much money does Greg provide in all?**

Ratio, Proportion, and Percent

Give Her a Centimeter, and She'll Take a Meter

Elissa's height is 80% of Susan's height. Marci's height is 75% of Susan's height. If Marci is 8 centimeters shorter than Elissa, how tall is Susan?

Choose or Lose

There are 2125 students at Beethoven Bay High School. The students in one of the school's music classes surveyed 25 randomly chosen students to determine their music preferences. Of these students, eight named hip-hop as their favorite musical style. Based on these results, how many students in the entire school would be expected to name hip-hop as their favorite musical style?

Clean Clothes for Less

Tired of having their clothes come out wrinkled and smelling of cat hair, the Phillips family bought a new washer/dryer combo. The washer's original cost was $490, but it was on sale for 10% off. The dryer cost $300. It was not on sale, but Mom Phillips found a small chip in the enamel and got the sales staff to give them a discount. If the total cost of the washer and the dryer was $726, what percentage discount did the Phillips family receive on the dryer?

Mmmmm, Mmmmm, Good

A candy jar contains chocolate candies and hard candies. Hard candies make up 40% of the contents of the jar. Mary Ellen eats 25% of the chocolate candies and replaces them with an equal number of hard candies. What percentage of the candies in the jar are hard candies now?

Greed vs. Power

A political pollster asks 100 randomly chosen registered voters for their preferences in the next city council election, which pits Gerald Greed against Patti Power. Thirty of those people say they do not intend to vote in this contest. Based on the views of the rest, the pollster predicts that Greed will win, because 60% of those polled favored his policies. How many people in the sample expressed a preference for Greed over Power?

One Is Good, Two Is Better

A pair of shoes ordinarily costs $48. During a summer sale, however, the price is reduced by 35%. Barry buys two pairs of the shoes. How much do the two pairs cost together?

She Shoots, She Scores

The Bay Ridge Bulldogs score 78 points in a basketball game against the Sunset Ridge Serpents. During the game, the Bulldogs score on 90% of their free throws, 45% of their field goals, and 25% of their three-point shots. Each free throw is worth 1 point, each field goal 2 points, and each three-point shot 3 points. If the Bulldogs attempt 20 free throws and 60 field goals, how many three-point goals did the team attempt?

Philo Milo Rocks

In 2003, the band Philo Milo sells a certain number of CDs. The following year, the band sells 20% fewer CDs than it did in 2003. In 2005, the band sells exactly as many CDs as it sold in 2003. **By what percent did Philo Milo's CD sales increase between 2004 and 2005?**

Watch Your Money Grow ... Slowly

At the end of August, Alannah opened a bank account with $1850 she had earned from her summer job canning tomatoes. Over the next year, she neither withdrew any of the funds nor deposited any more money in that account. If she earned 2% interest on her money during that time, how much money did she have in her account after one year?

It's a Grand Old Game

Sharlene loves to play Parcheesi with her friend Zoë. One summer weekend when there is nothing good on TV, they complete 36 games. Sharlene wins 22 games, and there are no draws or ties. What is the ratio of Sharlene's wins to Zoë's wins?

The DVD Nobody Wanted

A store offers a DVD for sale at a list price of $22, then sweetens the deal by advertising 15% off. When no one wants to buy the DVD, even at the sale price, the store reduces the price by an additional 10%. What is the current selling price of the DVD?

The Overpopulated Pond

A pond contains 38 goldfish and 77 other fish. How many goldfish must be added to the pond so that goldfish will make up 45% of the total fish in the pond?

Picasso, Jr.

At McKenzie High School, seven students take art for every four students who take music. If 312 students take music, how many students take art?

Say Cheese!

Veronica buys a camera on sale at 30% off the regular price. The store adds 5% sales tax to the price Veronica pays. Veronica's total bill is $191.10. What is the original price of the camera?

An Exponential Headache

For fun, Aaron and Erin are each assigned a positive integer greater than 2. They each know their own numbers, but neither knows the other person's number. They both know, however, that Aaron's number is less than Erin's. Which is greater, (Aaron's number)$^{\text{(Erin's number)}}$ or (Erin's number)$^{\text{(Aaron's number)}}$? Can the answer even be determined?

Microbe Alert

A scientist places a population of 500 microbes in a petri dish for further study. The population of the microbes grows by 25% every hour. After 9 hours, how many microbes are there?

Just Cube It

Babs chooses two integers and writes them on a card. She tells you that one of the integers is positive and the other is negative. If you raise each of the numbers to the third power and then multiply the results, what must be true about your answer?

Small, Smaller, Smallest

A scientist describes the radius of a small object as 3×10^{-5} millimeters. What is this number written in standard notation?

Shrivelsville

Because of a lack of jobs and an unhealthy climate, the town of Shrivelsville loses 4% of its population every year. If Shrivelsville had 10,000 people in 1990, what was its population in 2005? Round the population to the nearest hundred.

A Population Problem

The population of a certain country is 2.58×10^6. Exactly half of those people live in the capital city, and the rest live elsewhere. How many people live in the capital city?

A Logarithm Here, a Logarithm There

Place the digits 2, 4, 5, and 6 into the blanks to make the following statement true:

$\log_{[\underline{}]} \underline{} \; \underline{} 5 = \underline{}.$

The Leprechaun's Pot of Gold

There are 4^{38} pieces of gold inside a leprechaun's pot. When the number of gold pieces in the pot is written as an integer, which digit will be in the units, or ones, place?

Make More Money

A savings bank offers investors a 1.5% return on their savings per month. Morgan opens a savings account with $2000. How much money will she have in her account at the end of one year?

That's a Lot of Rats

Four lab rats stage a daring escape in broad daylight, eventually establishing a colony behind the laboratory's parking garage. After one month, the population of the colony has risen to eight rats. After two months, the population is 16; after three months, 32, and so on. If the pattern continues, how many months will it take for the colony population to reach 1024 rats?

Coming and Going

On his way to work, Mr. Charles travels 60 miles in $1\frac{1}{4}$ hours. On his way home, Mr. Charles travels the same distance in $1\frac{1}{2}$ hours. What is the difference, in miles per hour, between his rate of speed going to work and his rate of speed coming home from work?

Riding a Country Mile

When Javier zips down country roads on his bicycle, it takes him 40 minutes to go 8 miles. When he drives his car, Javier travels twice as far in two-fifths the time. What is Javier's speed, in miles per hour, when he drives his car?

Signature Salads

The specialty dish at the Cool Café is Signature Salad, which includes a long list of ingredients that only a few people have ever heard of. However, the dish is extremely popular, as it is widely believed to make the eater truly cool. Hank and Oscar are the chief salad makers. Hank can make 14 Signature Salads in an hour, and Oscar can make eight Signature Salads in 30 minutes. How many Signature Salads can they make together in $1\frac{1}{2}$ hours?

The Long Journey of the Plastic Knife

The Lazy River flows downstream at a rate of 0.6 kilometers per hour. A picnicker accidentally drops a plastic knife in the river at 12:45 P.M. At 6:15 P.M. that evening, an angler fishes the plastic knife out of the river. How far did the knife travel?

Rates and Speed

Fiction Is Faster

Miriam reads at an average rate of 80 pages per hour when reading fiction and 48 pages per hour when reading nonfiction. Last night she read for 2 hours. During that time, she read the same number of pages of fiction as she read of nonfiction. How many minutes did she spend reading fiction?

Sew Me the Slippers!

Six workers can make 30 pairs of slippers in 4 hours. How many hours will it take three other workers to make 60 pairs of slippers if they work at the same pace as the original six workers?

ASDFG HJKL

Each year the local Association of Typists holds a typing competition to crown a typing champion. Participants are given an extremely boring document by the Typing Committee and are asked to input the document into their computers as quickly as possible. This year, the document dealt with banana slugs and was 2772 words long. The winner typed the entire document in 1680 seconds. What was the winner's average rate of speed in words typed per minute?

Brownsville to Bluesville

Upon reaching its cruising altitude, a passenger jetliner moves at a speed of 620 miles per hour. The plane maintains this speed from the time it is directly above Brownsville to the time it is directly above Bluesville—a distance of 775 miles. How many minutes does it take the plane to cover this distance?

Handymen and Handywomen

It takes two carpenters six days to build four decks. Assuming that the rate of work remains the same, how many decks can five carpenters build in nine days?

Peeled Potatoes

Sheila can peel five potatoes in 6 minutes. At that rate, how long will it take her to peel 22 potatoes? Express your answer in minutes and seconds.

Chantal Takes a Trip

Chantal drives from Mountain Village to Mountain City. The whole trip takes 6 hours, including a 30-minute stop for lunch when she is exactly halfway between the two cities. She drives at a steady rate of 60 miles per hour before lunch and drives at a steady rate of 50 miles per hour afterward. How many miles does Chantal drive in total?

A Problem of Youth

Emily is twice as old as Matt. Three years ago, she was three times as old as he was. **How old is Matt now?**

Algebra

Mr. McGillicuddy's Mack Truck

On average, Mr. McGillicuddy's Mack truck travels 9.5 miles on 1 gallon of gas. Last Thursday, Mr. McGillicuddy used the truck to haul a load of marshmallow peeps to McAllister. The distance from Mr. McGillicuddy's garage to McAllister is 228 miles. How many gallons of gas does Mr. McGillicuddy use while driving to McAllister?

Patriotic Paola

A flagpole is m feet high. Paola places the flagpole on a flat deck that is $2m - 11$ feet above the ground. Then she raises the flag to 4 feet below the top of the pole. In terms of m, how far off the ground is the flag?

Algebra

Regular or Decaf?

Unlike more modern coffee franchises, Aunt Margaret's Coffee Shop offers just two kinds of coffee: regular and decaf. One Thursday morning, Aunt Margaret's sold 184 cups of coffee to its customers. The shop's staff sold 48 more cups of regular than they sold cups of decaf. How many cups of decaf did the staff sell that day?

Another Problem of Youth

This year, Serena is one-seventh of her cousin's age. Two years from now, Serena will be one-fourth of her cousin's age. In how many years will Serena be half her cousin's age?

Algebra

Random Equations from Robert and Roberta

Robert and Roberta each write an equation at random. Robert writes $y = 3x + 6$. Roberta writes $6x + 2y = 8$. For what value of x do the two equations each give the same value for y?

Bragging Rights

There are 363 students at Meadowbrook High School. There are 10 more freshmen than sophomores, 20 more juniors than sophomores, and seven more seniors than freshmen. **How many seniors are there at the school?**

Mind Your F's and G's

If $f(x) = x^2$ and $g(x) = \frac{x}{2}$, what is the difference between $g(f(6))$ and $f(g(6))$?

He's Only Just Begun

Victor has just gotten a new iPod. So far, he has loaded 73 songs onto it. Each of these 73 songs belongs to one of two musical styles: bluegrass and show tunes. If he has 21 more bluegrass songs than show tunes, how many show tunes are on his iPod so far?

Algebra

For the Birds

While hiking in a national park, Jane saw n orioles, $2n + 5$ cardinals, and $3n - 9$ blue jays. If she saw 18 blue jays, how many cardinals did she see?

The Wall

Swati hangs 11 posters on an empty wall in her bedroom. None of the posters overlaps the others, and all of the posters have the same dimensions. The wall is 10 feet long and 8 feet high. After hanging the posters, Swati has 14 square feet of empty wall space. If each poster is 1 foot longer than it is wide, what is the dimension of each poster?

Statistics Test Statistics

Sixteen students in a statistics class take a test. The 16 students receive 16 different whole number scores. Myron's score, 79, ranks him ninth in the class, just behind Miguel. If the median of the 16 scores is 81.5, what is Miguel's score on the test?

Homer Happy

The five outfielders on the Parkesville Panthers baseball team all hit for power. Together, they've hit 60 home runs so far this season. Marty Gonzalez leads with 17 home runs. Tommy Griswold has 10 home runs, fewer than any other Panther outfielder. How many homers have the other three outfielders hit? What are the mean, median, and mode of the five outfielders' homer stats?

King of the Pins

Ahmed's bowling scores are 213, 242, 199, and 185. If Ahmed has a five-game score of 200 or more, he qualifies for the all-city tournament. Though bowling scores must be whole numbers, mean scores may turn out to be decimals. If the means do turn out to be decimals, they are rounded to the nearest whole number. What is the minimum score Ahmed must get in his next game to qualify for the all-city tournament?

A Matter of Degrees

To determine the mean high temperature during a certain period of time, take each day's high temperature during that period and find the mean of those temperatures. In the village of Cold Lake, the mean high temperature during one seven-day period was 6 degrees Fahrenheit. The daily high temperature during that period never dipped below 0 degrees F. What was the highest possible temperature recorded in Cold Lake during that seven-day period?

Mean, Median, and Mode

Don't Be Mean

The mean of a set of six numbers is 91. The mean of three of those numbers is 48. What is the mean of the other three numbers?

In Your Face: The Musical

Tickets to the latest Broadway hit, *In Your Face*, can be purchased for $65, $70, $75, $80, or $85, depending on how close to the stage you wish to sit. Julian sees the show three times. His mean ticket price is $75, and his median ticket price is $70. Elizabeth also sees the show three times. Her mean ticket price is $75, but her median ticket price is $80. Who purchased an $85 ticket?

Dumber, Poorer, Slower

Aidan takes four chemistry tests. His mean score on these four tests is 87. After Aidan takes a fifth chemistry test, his mean score for all five tests drops by two points. What is his score on the fifth test?

The State of Anxiety

All license plates issued by the State of Anxiety begin with a four-digit number ranging from 1000 to 9999 and conclude with two letters. What is the probability that all four digits in a randomly chosen license plate will be odd?

© 2006 SparkNotes LLC

A Friendly Wager

Hamlet writes the integers 1 through 15 on slips of paper and puts them in a bag. He invites his friend Othello to draw one slip at random. Hamlet promises to pay Othello $1 if Othello draws a slip with a number that is divisible by either 3 or 4. However, if Othello draws a slip with a number that is divisible by neither 3 nor 4, Othello must pay Hamlet $1. Who is most likely to win? Why?

Three Colors of Ink

A box contains nine pens. Of these pens, two are blue, three are red, and four are black. **How many pens must you pull out of the box to be certain that you have at least one pen of each color?**

The Mysterious Sock Drawer

Drew randomly draws a sock from his drawer. Of the socks in the drawer, $\frac{1}{3}$ are black, $\frac{1}{4}$ are brown, and the rest are white. **What is the probability that he draws a white sock?**

A Jolly Bag of Marbles

Wendy has one chance in six of drawing a blue marble from a bag of marbles. There are 48 marbles in the bag. **How many blue marbles does the bag contain?**

Valuable Prizes Will Be Awarded

Of the 39 students in the school orchestra, 21 play string instruments, 15 play wind instruments, and the rest play percussion. At the orchestra's annual picnic, four orchestra members are chosen at random to receive a valuable prize. The first three students whose names are chosen all play string instruments. What is the probability that the fourth student chosen will play a string instrument too?

That's Mr. Jelly Belly to You

Thalia fills some snack bags with jelly beans. Some of the bags contain only plum jelly beans. Other bags contain only red apple jelly beans. The rest contain only pear jelly beans. Because she likes flavorful surprises, Thalia puts all of the bags into a box. Later that afternoon, she pulls out one bag at random. She has one chance in five of pulling out a bag of plum jelly beans, and she is just as likely to pull a bag with red apple jelly beans as she is to pull a bag of pear jelly beans. If there are 18 bags of pear jelly beans in the box, how many bags of plum jelly beans are there in the box?

Baby Needs a New Pair of Shoes

Jed tosses two six-sided dice. Assuming that the dice are fair, what is the probability that both dice will show a number less than five?

A Fate Worse than Death

Trapped by aliens and at the mercy of their leader, Julio is told to first toss a fair six-sided die and then to toss a fair coin. According to the aliens, if the die comes up six *and* the coin comes up tails, he will be released. Otherwise, he will be forced to listen to disco music nonstop for the next 24 years. What is the probability that Julio will be released?

Probability

Book Him

A book has pages numbered from 1 to 146. As is standard for books, page 1 is a right-hand page, and page 146 is a left-hand page. Douglas opens the book at random to a two-page spread, which includes two numbered pages, neither of which is page 1 or page 146. What is the probability that the numbers on the two pages have a product that is even *and* a sum that is odd?

Who's Got the Edge?

Three people are playing darts. Sabrina hits the bull's-eye, on average, four times in every 13 shots. Garrett hits the bull's-eye twice in every seven shots. Maddy hits it three times in every eight shots. Rank the three players in order from the most likely to hit the bull's-eye to the least likely.

Geometry

Going the Distance

On the coordinate plane, what is the distance between the two points (6, 5) and (–2, –1)?

A Problem of Twos

A square is divided into two equal triangles. If the area of the square is 2 square inches, what is the length of the diagonal that divides it?

The Clock of Thymeville

In Thymeville, the city hall has a large clock. It is 8 feet from the tip of the second hand to the center of the clock. How many feet will the tip of the second hand move in an hour? (Use 3.14 for pi, then round to the nearest whole foot.)

Find Me a Sum, as Fast as You Can

The angles in a triangle add up to 180 degrees, the angles in a quadrilateral add up to 360 degrees, and the angles in a pentagon add up to 540 degrees. What is the sum of the angles in an octagon?

Tipping the Square

A square is positioned on a coordinate grid. One vertex of the square is at (5, 0). Another vertex is at (0, 9). **What is the area of the square?**

It's a Frame-Up

Latrelle has two long pieces of wood and two short pieces of wood. He would like to use them to make a rectangular picture frame for his latest art-class masterpiece. The perimeter of the frame will be 32 inches, and the area of the frame will be 48 square inches. What is the length of the two short pieces of wood?

The Perimeter's Area

A certain rectangle has an area of 128 square centimeters. The rectangle is divided into two equal squares. What is the perimeter of the original rectangle?

Meet at the Right Angle

Sybil is using a new geometry computer program to practice her math skills. First, Sybil sketches the equation $y = -\frac{1}{3}x$. Next, the computer shows her the equation $y = mx$. Then it asks her to identify the value of m that will create a line perpendicular to the original line. **What is this value of m?**

Bill Me Later

Chuck does simple carpentry jobs for his neighbors. He charges $6.50 an hour for his labor and includes a flat fee for each project's supplies. He contracts with Mr. Snow to build a set of shelves. At the end of the project, he presents Mr. Snow with a bill for $112, which includes $34 in supplies. How many hours did Chuck spend on the project?

Reach Out and Touch Someone

Ms. James does computer consulting. She charges an hourly rate to help people learn to use the internet and offers a senior citizen discount of $10 off the total bill to help entice grandparents who wish to keep in touch with their busy, wired grandchildren. Mr. Yawls, one of her best customers, qualifies for the senior citizen discount. If Ms. James earns $226.25 for 15 hours of work with Mr. Yawls, what is her hourly rate?

An Apple a Day

Sam has a prescription medicine plan in which he pays either $15 or $25 for each prescription. Last year, he purchased 15 different medications and paid a total of $355. How many $25 medications did he buy?

Going Nuts

A store sells gourmet nuts by the pound. Matilda buys a bag containing 20 ounces of nuts. The bag costs a total of $6.25. What is the cost of the nuts per pound? (There are 16 ounces in 1 pound.)

Logging On for Less

At the convention center's internet kiosk, it costs $2.50 to log on for up to 5 minutes. Each additional minute online costs 35 cents. Ryder goes online at the kiosk and spends a total of $9.85. How many minutes in all did she spend online?

Adventures in Economics

During the fall term, there are a certain number of students in an economics class. Of these students, $\frac{3}{8}$ are sophomores and the rest are juniors. At the beginning of the spring term, one sophomore transfers out of the class and two juniors transfer in. Now sophomores make up $\frac{1}{3}$ of the class. How many students are enrolled in the class during the fall term?

The Umbrella Room

Sal sells fruit salad from a pushcart known as the Umbrella Room, because of its canopy. She charges $2.95 per container. One morning she earns $300.90 from the sale of fruit salad. How many containers did she sell?

Addicted to Soup

Cans of mushroom soup are on sale for 45 cents each. Cans of tomato soup are on sale for 40 cents each. Dale buys 23 cans of soup and pays a total of $9.70, not including sales tax. **If Dale buys only mushroom and tomato soup, how many more cans of tomato soup than cans of mushroom soup does Dale buy?**

Talk Is Cheap

Every month the phone company charges long-distance rates of 9 cents a minute, plus a fixed administrative fee. This month, Queenisha is charged for 104 minutes of long-distance calls. Her total bill for the month is $13.86. What is the administrative fee?

Doesn't She Need Dryers?

At Handy Hardware, Inc., large washers cost 7 cents apiece and small washers cost 5 cents apiece. For a do-it-yourself project, Rhonda needs to buy washers. She has $2.60. If she wants to buy exactly three large washers for every small washer she buys, how many small washers can she purchase? (Rhonda lives in a no–sales tax state.)

The HVHS PTA

There are 87 dues-paying members of the Parent-Teacher Association at Harper Valley High School. Of these 87, there are 41 more women than men. How many men are dues-paying members of this organization?

Answer the Phone!

Molly received n telephone calls last week. Her sister Shawna received five fewer calls than Molly, and her sister LeeAnn received twice as many calls as Shawna. Write an expression in terms of n to show how many calls the three sisters received in all last week. (Be sure to simplify the equation.)

A Birthday Conundrum

While planning a birthday party for her young nephew Willy, Aunt Bea is faced with a problem: which company should she hire to handle the festivities? Patty's Party Patrol charges $30 per hour for a 4-hour party, with a surcharge of $10 for each child after the first eight. Betty's Birthday Bash charges $35 per hour for a 4-hour party, with a $5 surcharge for each child after the first eight. For which number of children will the costs of both party planners be precisely the same?

A Problem of CDs

Audra owns m CDs. Her cousins Bill, Chandra, and Dave own, respectively, $m + 2$ CDs, $4m - 21$ CDs, and $\frac{m}{2} + 8$ CDs. If Chandra owns three more CDs than Audra, which of the four owns the greatest number of CDs?

WORD PROBLEMS

A Night at the Movies

Ms. Schorr is planning a night at the movies for a group of families in her neighborhood. The theater usually charges $8 for adults and $5 for children ages 12 and under. There is a special group rate of $6 per ticket available, though the group rate doesn't include discounts for children. Ms. Schorr needs to buy 31 tickets. After figuring out the comparative costs of the regular rate versus the group rate, she realizes that the group rate is a better deal. What is the maximum number of children included in the group?

Thistlebottom's Thistle Removal

Thistlebottom's Thistle Removal Service charges $22 an hour plus a materials fee of $36. Write an equation showing the cost in dollars, D, for the number of hours, h, Thistlebottom's Thistle Removal Service spends on the job.

Eager Readers

For homework last night, Ms. Grande assigned her students to read at least n pages in their English literature books. Tricia read $n + 25$ pages, and Saad read $2n - 3$ pages. If Saad read more pages than Tricia, what is the smallest possible value of n?

The Cost of Flight

On a long flight with no movie, three airline travelers compare notes. They discover that they all paid different prices for their tickets. The most expensive ticket cost $257.50. The least expensive cost $10 more than half as much as the most expensive ticket. If the mean price of the three tickets was $200, what was the median price of the tickets?

So Many Letters, So Small a Mean

The mean of *a* and *b* is 52. The mean of *c* and *d* is 24. The sum of *e* and *f* is 40. What is the mean of *a*, *b*, *c*, *d*, *e*, and *f*?

House Numbers

In a certain town, streets that run north to south have odd-numbered houses on the west side of the street and even-numbered houses on the east side of the street. Oak Terrace runs just one block from north to south and includes houses numbered from 1 to 19. There are no missing house numbers or empty spaces. On which side of the street is the mean of the house numbers greater?

Pawn to Queen's Knight 4

Four retired friends meet in the park each day to play chess. The mode of their ages is 58. The median of their ages is 62. Ronald, the most senior member of the group, turned 70 on his last birthday. What is the mean of their ages?

That's What I Mean

The mean of 2, 5, and a is equal to the mean of 4, 8, and b. How much greater than b is a?

Eat at the Sandwich Shoppe

Sierra's Sandwich Shoppe is open each weekday. On Monday, the clerks at the shop sold 70 sandwiches. On Tuesday, they sold half as many sandwiches as they sold on Wednesday and Friday combined. On Wednesday, they sold five fewer sandwiches than they sold on Thursday. On Thursday, they sold five more sandwiches than they sold on Friday. On Friday, they sold five more sandwiches than they sold on Monday. What is the mode of the sandwich-selling data?

Means to Multiply

The mean of a set of numbers is 3.25. If every number in the set is multiplied by 10, what will the mean of the new set be?

Achtung!

For homework in German class, Frau Beiler assigns her students to write poems in German. The poems must have a maximum of 24 lines and a minimum of 16, and each poem must have an even number of lines. If exactly half the students write poems that are 18 lines long, what is the greatest possible median of the data? What is the least possible median?

Comparing Functions

A function $f(x)$ is defined as $f(x) = x^3$. A function $g(x)$ is defined as $g(x) = 3^x$. For the following values of x, indicate whether $f(x)$ or $g(x)$ is greater:

$x = 1$

$x > 3$

$x < 0$

Cutting the Ribbon

A ribbon is 2^7 inches long. Delores cuts it into 4^3 equal pieces. How many inches long is each piece?

A Most Unusual X

For most values of x, $x^5 < x^6$. What is one value of x for which $x^5 > x^6$?

In Terms of *N*

If m and n are both prime numbers, how many factors does m^n have? Give your answer in terms of n.

Interesting Intersections

On the coordinate plane, at which two points does the graph of $y = x^2$ intersect the graph of $y = x^3$?

That's a Lot of Customers

A mammoth chain store's database of customers includes 9^4 names. The list is divided into 3^4 shorter lists, each containing the same number of names. How many names are on each of the shorter lists?

Light as a Frisbee

A group of plastic disks is placed in a container. All the plastic disks are the same weight. Three plastic disks, together with the container, weigh 5 ounces. Eleven plastic disks, together with the same container, weigh 9 ounces. What is the weight of a single plastic disk?

Build Me a Walkway as Fast as You Can

Benson can build a cement walkway in 6 hours. If he starts at noon and works without stopping at a constant pace, at what time will he have completed $\frac{5}{12}$ of the walkway?

Don't Try This at Home

A certain metal is cooled to a temperature of –12 degrees F, then placed into a heated oven. The temperature of the metal rises at a steady rate of $4m$, where m represents the number of minutes that the metal has been in the oven. If the metal is placed into the oven at 9:45 A.M., at what time will its temperature reach 52 degrees F?

Heavy Metal

A metal plate is manufactured to **weigh a certain number** of kilograms. A box of 15 of these metal plates weighs 35 kilograms, which includes the weight of the metal plates as well as the weight of the box itself. When five of the metal plates have been removed from the box, **the box and the remaining metal plates** weigh 24 kilograms. What is the weight of the box?

The Discoveries of Lily Padd

While working with a newly discovered form of pond life, medical researcher Lily Padd makes an interesting finding: the life form triples in volume each day. How many times larger will the life form be on Monday than it was on the previous Friday?

Truck vs. SUV

A truck and an SUV leave the civic center at 1:00 P.M. and head west to the same destination, which is 140 miles away. The truck arrives at this destination at 3:30 P.M. that same afternoon. The SUV arrives 1 hour afterward. Measured in miles per hour, what is the average difference in the speed of the truck and the speed of the SUV?

Building with Blocks

A six-year-old is building a vertical tower with cubes. She places the first cube on a low table, which is resting on the floor, and stacks the other blocks on top of the first. She stops when the height of the tower is exactly even with the top of her head. If the height of the six-year-old is represented by h, the number of cubes is represented by n, and the height of each cube is represented by c, write an expression to find t, the height of the tabletop.

Swim, Gofast, Swim

While swimming across a lake, champion distance swimmer G. I. Gofast swims at a rate of 1.6 miles per hour when she is swimming with the current, but only at a rate of 1.2 miles per hour when she is swimming against the current. She spends half her time in the water swimming with the current and the rest of her time swimming against it. If the entire swim takes her 21 hours, how many miles does she swim in all?

Quiz Show Deadline

Fred needs to write 496 trivia questions for a famous TV show. He begins the assignment on July 1 and needs to finish it on the last day of August. His intent is to write an equal number of questions each day and complete question #496 on August 31. However, the beach beckons, and just before midnight on July 31 Fred realizes that he is well behind schedule. In fact, during July he has written only half of the questions he had planned to write by July 31. How many questions will Fred need to write each day during August so that he will complete all 496 trivia questions by August 31?

Sum Numbers

Three different positive integers have a sum of 210. The least of these integers is 69. What is the product of the other two integers?

Perfect Daughter Squares

Ginnie's current age is twice that of her daughter. Next year, Ginnie's age will be a perfect square, as will her daughter's. How old is Ginnie's daughter this year?

Red, Yellow, Green, Go

A certain stoplight is red for 27 seconds, then green for 15 seconds, and yellow for 3 seconds before beginning the cycle again. One Saturday afternoon the light turns green at precisely 2:07 P.M. What color will the light turn at precisely 2:10 P.M.? What color will it turn at precisely 2:11 P.M.?

A Little More Each Day

This week, Kwame plans to run a total of 90 or more laps at the school track. He plans to begin on Monday by running a certain number of laps. Every day after that through Sunday, he will add one lap to the previous day's total. What is the smallest number of laps Kwame must run on Monday to reach his goal?

Product Placement

Two positive integers have a sum of 49. What is the greatest possible product of the two integers?

What Remains of the Day

When a certain positive integer q is divided by p, the remainder is 3. When $q + 3$ is divided by p, the remainder is 1. What is the value of p?

To a T

Vinnie has seven T-shirts in his drawer. He grabs one at random to wear on his daily run. When he comes home, he grabs a second T-shirt to change into after his shower. Four of the shirts are white, and the rest are blue. What is the probability that Vinnie runs in a blue shirt and changes into a white shirt after his shower?

The Mailbox Problem

Each of the seven student council members at Victor High School has his or her own labeled mailbox outside the assistant principals' shared office. One of the assistant principals writes a personal note to each of the seven students but then accidentally places the seven notes into the mailboxes at random. If each student receives one note, what is the probability that exactly six of the students receive the note intended for them?

Fair or Unfair?

Jessie and Eva play a game with two six-sided dice. Each player rolls one die. If the product of the two rolls is even, Jessie gets a point. If the product of the two rolls is odd, Eva gets a point. What is the probability that Eva will win any given point?

Alpha Baking Order

Ruthie needs to call her friends Spencer, Timothy, and Ursula to remind them to bring in goodies for the bake sale. If she makes the calls at random, what is the probability that she will call the friends in alphabetical order (that is, in the order given above)? (Assume that all three friends have different phone numbers.)

ISO a RSB

Leah is asked to get a red sleeping bag out of the back seat of her mother's car. There are seven sleeping bags in the car, only two of which are red. All the bags are in black, zippered cases, so there is no way to tell which sleeping bag is which without opening the cases. Leah picks s cases, with $s < 5$, and discovers that not one of these cases contains a red sleeping bag. She tosses each of these cases into the front seat of the car. In terms of s, what is the probability that the next case Leah chooses from the back seat will contain a red sleeping bag?

The Light Bulb

Fuad keeps a light bulb burning at all times on his front porch. After many days of being on, the light bulb will stop working. If the probability is $\frac{3}{4}$ that the light bulb will stop working at a time when Fuad is awake, how many hours a day, on average, does Fuad sleep?

Can It!

A cooler contains six cans of diet pop and three cans of regular pop. Bob takes two cans out of the cooler at random. What is the probability that both cans will contain diet pop?

Vroom, Vroom, Shift

The latest model of the Spider QX237 luxury sports car comes with a choice of automatic or standard transmission. Of the 100 orders placed for the car during April, 64 are for a model with standard transmission. If that proportion holds, how many of the 625 orders placed during May will be for a model with standard transmission?

I'll Think about It Tomorrow....

Scarlett buys a mansion for $475,000. One year later, taking advantage of a hot housing market, she sells the property. After paying a 5% real estate agent's fee, she has a profit of $95,000. Not including the real estate agent's fee, what was the selling price of the mansion?

I Scream, You Scream

An ice cream vendor sells ice cream pints in three flavors: strawberry, vanilla, and chocolate. The vendor's freezer contains 50 pints in all. The pints are in the ratio 2:3:5, with more chocolate than vanilla and more vanilla than strawberry. How many pints of vanilla does the vendor have?

The Oppressive Party

The legislature of a certain country has 239 members. Five of these members belong to the Autocratic Party. The rest belong to either the Oppressive Party or the Domineering Party in the ratio 9:4. How many members, in all, do NOT belong to the Oppressive Party?

High School Intramurals

At a certain school, 17% of the students play intramural volleyball and 12% of the students play intramural soccer. Eight students play both intramural volleyball and intramural soccer. If 75% of the student body plays neither intramural volleyball nor intramural soccer, how many students go to the school?

168 *DAILY SPARK · MATH WORD PROBLEMS*

Terminators Win! Terminators Win!

Last season, the Terminators hockey team won 60% of the games in which they scored at least three goals, but only 15% of the games in which they scored two goals or one goal. They scored at least three goals twice as often as they scored two goals or one goal, and they won no games when they scored no goals. If they won two games in which they scored two goals and one game in which they scored one goal, how many games did they win during the 80-game season?

Tulips Together

A row of tulips includes 24 red tulips and a certain number of yellow tulips. If yellow tulips make up 60% of the tulips in the row, how many yellow tulips are there?

Golden Goal Scorers

The field hockey team at Golden High School includes a certain number of players. Of these players, 35% are seniors, 25% juniors, and 15% are sophomores. The remaining five players are freshmen. **How many seniors are on the team?**

Dehydration? No Thanks

Gladys buys 48 bottles of water for the track meet. It costs 75 cents to buy an individual bottle, but the store sells packages of 12 bottles for $7.20. How much money would Gladys spend if she purchased 48 individual bottles? How much money would she save if she bought packages of 12 bottles instead?

Call the Quarry

As a community project, a school group is building a playground in a local park. The playground will be constructed on a rectangular area measuring 30 feet by 16 feet. For safety reasons, there needs to be an average of 5 inches of gravel spread on the dirt across the entire playground. How many cubic feet of gravel will be needed?

Timing the Trip

Ivan is driving from his home to West Spinach. It takes him 6 hours to drive the first 372 miles, which brings him exactly 93 miles past the halfway point between his home and his destination. If he drives at a steady rate throughout the journey, how long will the entire trip last?

The Crack o' Dawn

Charlie has to leave for school at 6:45 A.M. If he needs $\frac{1}{3}$ of an hour to shower, $\frac{1}{4}$ of an hour to get dressed, $\frac{1}{5}$ of an hour to eat breakfast, and $\frac{1}{6}$ of an hour to pack his lunch, at what time must he get out of bed in order to leave for school on time?

Filling the Fish Tank

Kathy has an aquarium that holds 96 pints of water. To fill the aquarium, she fills a 1-gallon container and pours the contents into the aquarium. How many times must she fill the container in order to fill the aquarium?

WORD PROBLEMS

Bulk Rate

Five friends want to buy packages of baseball cards. The card dealer is offering the packages for sale at $2.25 apiece. However, the store has a special bulk rate deal in which 10 packages of cards can be purchased for $19. If the friends buy a total of 40 packages at the bulk rate and share both the packages and the cost equally, how much money will each of the friends save compared to the cost of the packs if purchased individually?

Don't Fence Me In

A landscaper is building a rectangular garden that has an area of 48 square meters. She places a 38-meter fence around the garden to enclose it completely. What are the dimensions of the garden?

Money and Measurement

Yards to Inches

A board is 108 inches long. It is cut into p equal pieces. In terms of p, how many yards long is each piece?

Movie I and Movie II

A movie is 10 minutes and 20 seconds longer than its sequel. If the two movies together have a running time of 4 hours, 10 minutes, and 20 seconds, how long is the sequel?

Answers

1. **6 inches**

length × width × height = volume

$a \times \frac{a}{2} \times \frac{a}{3} = 36$

$\frac{a^3}{6} = 36$

$a^3 = 36 \times 6 = 6^3$

$a = 6$

2. **The circle**

The area of the circle = $pi(r^2)$ = $pi(3^2)$ = 9(pi) square inches. If the diagonal of the square is 6, then $6^2 = a^2 + a^2$, where a is the length of a side.

$36 = 2a^2$

$18 = a^2$

$a = (\sqrt{18})$

Therefore, the area of the square is $(\sqrt{18})^2$ = 18 square inches. Since pi > 3, the area of the circle > 27, so the area of the circle is greater.

3. **They both are. The two triangles have the same mean.**

The sum of the angles in every triangle is always 180 degrees, regardless of the type of triangle. Dividing 180 by 3 gives a mean of 60 for both triangles.

4. **Nine times larger**

The perimeter of the original square was 8 inches. Therefore, each side was 2 inches.

2 inches × 2 inches = 4 square inches area

In the new square, the length of the original side is tripled, so each side = 3 × 2 = 6 inches.

6 inches × 6 inches = 36 square inches area

$\frac{36}{4} = 9$

5. **8 points**

If the ellipse is laid on top of the rectangle so that it crosses each

181

side twice, there will be eight points of interception in all.

6. **(−4, 6)**

The sides of the square are 7 units long [$6 - (-1) = 6 + 1 = 7$, and $3 - (-4) = 3 + 4 = 7$]. The dogcatcher's house must be 7 units to the left of the mayor's home and 7 units above the town clerk's home, or at (−4, 6).

7. $k(\sqrt{5})$

The keyboard's dimensions are k and $2k$. To find the diagonal, find the square root of $k^2 + (2k)^2 = k^2 + 4k^2 = 5k^2$.

$x = \sqrt{k^2 + (2k)^2}$
$x = \sqrt{k^2 + 4k^2}$
$x = \sqrt{5k^2}$, or $k(\sqrt{5})$

182

8. **9**

$x + (2x - 3) + (x + 2) + (3x - 6) = 28$
$x + 2x + x + 3x - 3 + 2 - 6 = 28$
$7x - 7 = 28$
$7x = 35$
$x = 5$

Therefore, the lengths are 5, 7, 7, and 9, of which 9 is the longest.

9. $y = 2x - 8$

Remember to use the form $y = mx + b$.

$m = \text{slope} = \dfrac{\text{rise}}{\text{run}} =$
$\dfrac{2 - [-2]}{5 - 3} = \dfrac{4}{2} = 2$
$b = y\text{-intercept} = -8$
$y = 2x - 8$

10. **144 blocks**

$4 \times 2 \times 1.5 = 12$ cubic inches per block

The box contains $12 \times 12 \times 12 = 1728$ cubic inches.

$\dfrac{1728}{12} = 144$

11. **51**

$\dfrac{235}{5} = 47$, so 47 is the middle integer. The integers are 43, 45, 47, 49, and 51, of which 51 is the greatest.

12. **21 players**

$15 + 12 - 6 = 21$

13. **86 shirts**

The smallest possible number of large shirts is 93, because 93 is the smallest integer greater than 92. So, since $93 + 92 = 185$, this leaves 173 shirts (358 total – 185 large and medium shirts) to be divided among extra-large and small: $\frac{173}{2} = 87$, so, at most, there are 86 small shirts.

14. **0**

Dividing $2k$ by 9 gives a remainder of $4 + 4$, or 8. Dividing $(2k + 1)$ by 9 will add 1 to the remainder, which is the same as a remainder of 0. Adding 9 more $(2k + 10)$ does not change the remainder.

15. **4**

2^2, or 4

Let $x = 9$.

$9 \div 7 = 1$, with a remainder of 2

$9^2 = 81$

$81 \div 7 = 11$, with a reminder of 4

16. **27**

$\frac{360}{4} = 90$

There are three possible combinations of positive numbers whose product is 90 if both factors are greater than 4: 9×10, 6×15, and 5×18. Among these equations, 5×18 gives the greatest sum. The sum of 5, 18, and 4 is 27.

17. **72 laps**

Twelve laps take $12 \times 25 = 300$ seconds = 5 minutes. Adding in the 2-minute rest time (5 minutes + 2 minutes), a total swim cycle takes 7 minutes. According to the information given, Sheppard is in the pool for a total of 40 minutes: $\frac{40}{7} = 5$, with a remainder of 5. In this last 5 minutes, he swims another set of laps, so, in total, he swims 6 sets of 5 laps, or $6 \times 12 = 72$.

18. The Dukes scored **one field goal and two touchdowns** $(4 + 9 + 9 = 22)$.

The Meadowlarks scored **four field goals and one touchdown** $(4 \times 4 + 9 = 16 + 9 = 25)$.

The headline is wrong, because it's not possible for a team to score exactly 23 points.

19. $-40°F = -40°C$

$x = \frac{9x}{5} + 32$

$\frac{-4x}{5} = 32$

$-4x = 160$

$x = -40$

20. 65 coins

$\frac{220}{2} = 110$, so there are 110 nickels and dimes, and there is $1.10 in pennies (110 pennies = $1.10).

$9.85 - $1.10 = $8.75, which is the total value of the nickels and dimes.

$n + d = 110$, so $n = 110 - d$

$5n + 10d = 875$, so by substitution, $5(110 - d) + 10d = 875$.

$550 - 5d + 10d = 875$

$5d = 325$

$d = \frac{325}{5} = 65$

21. 16

4 yards = 12 feet

9 inches = $\frac{3}{4}$ feet

$12 ÷ \frac{3}{4} = 16$

22. $28.50

If it takes 4 minutes to dispense 9.5 gallons, 2.375 gallons are pumped in 1 minute ($\frac{9.5}{4} = 2.375$) and 14.25 gallons are pumped in 6 minutes ($2.375 × 6 = 14.25$).

To find out the cost of gas, multiply the gallons pumped by $2: $14.25 × $2 = 28.50.

23. 3.75 square feet

The wall is 6 feet × 10 feet = 60 sqare feet. All the stripes have the same dimensions, so $\frac{60}{16} = 3.75$.

24. $\frac{d}{xp}$

xp = total number of pencils

$\frac{d}{total}$ = cost per one pencil = $\frac{d}{xp}$

25. Bottle A has twice the volume of bottle B.

$Volume_{cylinder} = \pi r^2 h$

$V_A = \pi(2r)^2 h$

$V_B = \pi r^2(2h)$

184

$V_A = 4\pi r^2 h$

$V_B = 2\pi r^2 h$

So the volume of bottle A is twice as voluminous as the volume of bottle B.

26. **6.8 ounces**

$8 \times 0.85 = 6.8$

27. **40 times**

The ratio of scoring to not scoring is 5:3.

$5:3 = x:24$

$120 = 3x$

$x = 40$

28. **300 chainsaws**

$\frac{6}{100} = \frac{x}{5000}$

$30{,}000 = 100x$

$300 = x$

29. **30 members**

Let x = Mac users and y = PC users.

$3:2 = x:y$

$3y = 2x$

$x = \frac{3y}{2}$

Also, $x + y = 75$, so $\frac{3y}{2} + y = 75$

$\frac{5y}{2} = 75$

$5y = 150$

$y = 30$

30. $100\left[\frac{a}{j+a}\right]\%$

As a fraction, Ashley's share is $\frac{a}{j+a}$. To obtain a percent, multiply this fraction by 100.

31. $\frac{3}{5}$

$1.25m = 0.75n$

$m = \frac{0.75n}{1.25}$

$\frac{m}{n} = \frac{0.75}{1.25} = \frac{3}{5}$

32. **240 geese**

7 females:8 males

$7 \times 16 = 112$

$8 \times 16 = 128$

$112 + 128 = 240$

33. **$40.40**

$\$375 \times 1.06 = \$397.50$

$\$397.50 + \$6.50 = \$404$

$\$404 \times 1.10 = \$444.40$

$\$444.40 - \$404 = \$40.40$

34. **$2500**

The bake sale, scene-a-thon, and car wash accounted for 70% of the needed (36 + 20 + 14 = 70), so $750 represents 30% of the total.

$$\frac{30}{100} = \frac{750}{x}$$
$$30x = 75{,}000$$
$$x = 2500$$

35. 12 inches by 12 inches, or 1 foot × 1 foot

Black is the 2 in the 3:2:1 ratio. Green has half the area of black (2:1), so 24 square inches are green. Yellow has three times the area of green (3:1), so 72 square inches are green.

$$72 + 48 + 24 = 144$$

Because the flag is square, 144 square inches means sides of 12 inches each.

36. 40,700 people

$$\frac{7}{100} = \frac{2849}{x}$$
$$7x = 284{,}900$$
$$x = 40{,}700$$

37. 700 fruit flies

200 − 144 = 56, so $\frac{56}{2} = \frac{28}{100}$, or 28% of the fruit flies have vestigial wings.

$$\frac{28}{100} = \frac{x}{2500}$$
$$28(2500) = 100x$$
$$28(25) = x$$
$$700 = x$$

38. $1350

$4500 × 1.05 = $4,725

Malinda pays $\frac{3}{7}$ of the cost, so Ollie and Greg each provide $\frac{2}{7}$.

$\frac{1}{7}$ × $4725 = $625,
so $\frac{2}{7}$ × $4725 = $1350

39. 160 centimeters

5% of Susan's height = 8 centimeters
$$\frac{8}{0.05} = 8 \times 20 = 160$$

40. 680 students

8 of 25 = 32%
0.32(2125) = 680

41. 5%

$490 − $49 = $441, total paid for the washer
$726 − $441 = $285, total paid for the dryer

$300 – $285 = $15
$15 = 5% of $300

42. **55%**

0.75 × 0.60 = 0.45
1 – 0.45 = 0.55 = 55%

43. **42 people**

100 – 30 = 70 people
expressing a preference

60% of 70 is 42.

44. **$62.40**

$48 × 0.65 = $31.20, which is
the cost of one pair of shoes

$31.20 × 2 = $62.40

45. **8 goals**

90% of 20 = 18, so 18 points
from free throws
45% of 60 = 27, so 54 points
from field goals

18 + 54 = 72

78 – 72 = 6, so 6 points were
scored from three-point shots.

2 = 25% of x
$x = 8$

46. **25%**

If x = CD sales in 2003, then
0.80x = CD sales in 2004. The
increase between 2004 and
2005 can be expressed as $\frac{0.20}{0.80}$,
which equals 0.25, or 25%.

47. **$1887**

$1850 × 0.02 = $37
$1850 + $37 = $1887

48. **11:7**

If Sharlene wins 22 times,
Zoë wins 14 games.
22:14 reduces to 11:7.

49. **$16.83**

$22 × 0.85 = $18.70
$18.70 × 0.90 = $16.83

50. **25 fish**

Because only goldfish are to be
added, the 77 other fish must be
55% of the total number of fish.

$\frac{55}{100} = \frac{77}{x}$
$55x = 7700$
$x = 140$, which is the total
number of fish

140 − 77 = 63, which is the number of goldfish needed in all

63 − 38 = 25

51. 546 students

$7:4 = x:312$
$7(312) = 4x$
$2184 = 4x$
$x = 546$

52. $260

If x is the original price of the camera, then $0.7x$ is the sale price and $1.05(0.7x)$ is the price including sales tax.

$1.05(0.7x) = 191.10$
$0.735x - 191.10$
$0.735x = \frac{191.10}{0.735} = x$
$x = 260$

188

53. (Aaron's number)[(Erin's number)]

Test it out to verify:
$3^4 = 81$, while $4^3 = 64$
$3^5 = 243$, while $5^3 = 125$
$4^6 = 4096$, while $6^4 = 1296$

54. 3725 microbes

$500 \times (1 + 0.25)^9 = 500 \times (1.25)^9$
$500 \times 7.4506 \approx 3725$ microbes

55. Your answer will be negative.

A negative integer raised to the third power is negative, while a positive integer raised to the third power is positive. Multiplying a negative number by a positive number will produce a negative number.

56. 0.00003 millimeter

$10^{-5} = 0.00001$
$0.00001 \times 3 = 0.00003$

57. 5400 people

$10,000 \times (1 - 0.04)^{15} =$
$10,000 \times 0.96^{15} =$
$10,000 \times 0.542086 =$ about 5421

58. 1,290,000, or 1.29×10^6

$\frac{2.58}{2} = 1.29$

The magnitude of the number, as expressed by the exponent, does not change.

59. $\log[5]625 = 4$

Of the available digits, only 5 can produce a number ending in 5 with a nonfractional exponent: $5^4 = 625$. The other combinations (i.e., $5^2 = 25$, $5^6 =$ 15,625) do not work.

60. 6

The number 4 raised to any even exponent will always produce a number with 6 in the ones place. The best way to attempt a problem like this is by checking examples:

$4^2 = 16$
$4^3 = 64$
$4^4 = 256$
$4^5 = 1024$
$4^6 = 4096$

A pattern appears. When the exponent is even, there is a 6 in the ones place. Because 38 is even, the answer is 6.

61. Approximately $2391

$2000 \times (1 + 0.015)^{12} =$ $2000 \times (1.015)^{12}$, which is $\approx$ $2000 \times 1.1956 \approx 2391

62. 8 months

The population doubles once a month, so this is an example of powers of 2 beginning with 4: $4 \times 2 \times 2 \times 2 \times 2 \times 2 \times 2 \times 2 \times 2 = 1024$, or 8 months.

63. 8 miles per hour

Going to work: 60 miles $\div 1\frac{1}{4}$ hours = 60 miles $\div \frac{5}{4}$ hours = $\frac{60 \times 4}{5} = \frac{240}{5} = 48$ miles per hour

Coming home: 60 miles $\div 1\frac{1}{2}$ hours = 60 miles $\div \frac{3}{2}$ hours = $\frac{60 \times 2}{3} = \frac{120}{3} = 40$ miles per hour

48 miles per hour – 40 miles per hour = 8 miles per hour

64. 60 miles per hour

2×8 miles = 16 miles
$\frac{2}{5} \times 40$ minutes = 16 minutes
$\frac{16 \text{ miles}}{16 \text{ minutes}} = \frac{60 \text{ miles}}{60 \text{ minutes}} =$
60 miles per hour

65. 45 salads

Hank: $14 + \frac{14}{2} = 21$ salads in $1\frac{1}{2}$ hours
Oscar: $8 \times 3 = 24$ salads in $1\frac{1}{2}$ hours
$21 + 24 = 45$

66. 3.3 kilometers

$6:15 - 12:45 = 5.5$ hours, the length of the knife's trip

$5.5 \times 0.6 = 3.3$

67. 45 minutes

x = number of hours spent reading fiction

$80x = 48(2 - x)$

$80x = 96 - 48x$

$128x = 96$

$x = \frac{96}{128} = \frac{3}{4}$

$\frac{3}{4}$ of one hour = 45 minutes

68. 16 hours

Three workers sewing at the same pace will double the time needed to make 30 pairs to 8 hours. To make 60 slippers, the three workers would need to work for 16 hours.

69. 99 words per minute

$\frac{1680 \text{ seconds}}{60} = 28$ minutes

$\frac{2772 \text{ words}}{28 \text{ minutes}} = 99$ words per minute

70. 75 minutes

$\frac{775 \text{ miles}}{620 \text{ miles per hour}} = 1.25$ hours

1.25 hours = 1 hour 15 minutes

= 75 minutes

71. 15 decks

rate = $\frac{\text{work}}{\text{time}}$

rate = $\frac{4 \text{ decks}}{6 \text{ days}} = \frac{2 \text{ decks}}{3 \text{ days}}$, for

2 carpenters

$\frac{2}{3} \times 2.5 = \frac{5 \text{ decks}}{3 \text{ days}}$, for

5 carpenters

$\frac{5}{3} \times 9 = \frac{45}{3} = 15$ decks in 9 days

72. 26 minutes, 24 seconds

$22 \times \frac{6}{5} = \frac{132}{5} = 26\frac{2}{5}$ minutes = 26 minutes, 24 seconds

73. 300 miles

6 hours − 30 minutes = 5.5 hours total driving time

If x is the mileage before lunch, then $\frac{x}{60} + \frac{x}{50} = 5.5$ hours.

$\frac{5x + 6x}{300} = 5.5$

$11x = 1650$

$x = \frac{1650}{11} = 150$ miles

$150 + 150 = 300$

74. 6 years old

$E = 2M$ and $E - 3 = 3(M - 3)$

$2M = 3(M - 3) + 3$

$2M = 3M - 6$

$M = 6$

75. 24 gallons

$$\frac{228 \text{ miles}}{9.5 \text{ miles per gallon}} = 24 \text{ gallons}$$

76. 3m − 15

Flag = $(2m - 11) + (m - 4)$
F = $2m + m - 11 - 4$
F = $3m - 15$

77. 68 cups

$x + (x + 48) = 184$
$2x = 184 - 48$
$x = 68$

78. 10 years

7S = C and 4(S+2) = C + 2
7S = 4(S + 2) − 2
7S = 4S + 8 − 2
3S = 6
S = 2

Therefore, Serena is 2 years old this year and her cousin is 14. They are 12 years apart, so Serena will be half her cousin's age when Serena is 12 and her cousin is 24.

12 − 2 = 10 years

79. $x = -\frac{1}{3}$

Rewrite Roberta's equation in terms of y: $2y = 8 - 6x$
Reduce Roberta's equation:
$y = -3x + 4$
Set the right side of the equations equal to each other:
$-3x + 4 = 3x + 6$
$-6x = 2$
$-x = \frac{1}{3}$
$x = -\frac{1}{3}$

80. 96 seniors

Seniors = x
Freshmen = $x - 7$
Sophomores = $x - 17$
Juniors = $x + 3$

$x + (x - 7) + (x - 17) + (x + 3) = 363$
$4x - 21 = 363$
$4x = 384$
$x = 96$

81. 9

$f(6) = 6^2 = 36$
$g(36) = \frac{36}{2} = 18$, so $g(f(6)) = 18$
$g(6) = \frac{6}{2} = 3$
$f(3) = 3^2 = 9$, so $f(g(6)) = 9$
18 − 9 = 9

82. 26 show tunes

$s + (s + 21) = 73$
$2s + 21 = 73$

$2s = 52$

$s = 26$

83. 23 cardinals

$3n - 9 = 18$, so $3n = 27$

$n = 9$

$2(9) + 5 = 18 + 5 = 23$

84. 2 feet × 3 feet

$10 \times 8 = 80$ square feet of wall

$80 - 14 = 66$ sqare feet of wall

taken up with posters

$\frac{66 \text{ square feet}}{11 \text{ posters}} = 6$ square feet/

poster

2 feet × 3 feet = 6 sqare feet of

area/poster, with the length

1 foot longer than the width

85. 84

Myron is ninth, so Miguel is eighth. The median of 16 scores is the midpoint between the eighth and ninth. Thus, 81.5 is midway between Myron's and Miguel's score. Myron's score is 2.5 below the median (81.5 – 79 = 2.5), so Miguel's must be 2.5 above: 81.5 + 2.5 = 84.

86. 11 each; mean = 12, median = 11, mode = 11

Between them, Griswold and Gonzalez have 27 home runs (17 + 10 = 27). Since the five players have hit a combined 60, the other three players have hit 33 (60 – 27 = 33). Griswold has hit the fewest homers (10 total), so the other three players have hit 11 each

($\frac{33}{3} = 11$).

Mean = $\frac{60}{5} = 12$

Median = 11 = the central figure

Mode = 11 = the most common figure

87. 159

Ahmed needs 998 points to qualify, since $\frac{1000}{5} = 200$; $\frac{998}{5} = 199.6$, which rounds to 200; and $\frac{997}{5} = 199.4$, which rounds to 199.

He already has 839 points (213 + 242 + 199 + 185 = 839), so he needs to score a 159 in his next game (998 – 839 = 159).

88. 42°F

If the mean for the 7-day period was 6°F, then the total number of degrees during the period was $7 \times 6 = 42$. To obtain the highest possible temperature reading on one day, you need to assume that each of the other six days had the lowest possible high temperature, or 0°F. If six days had high temperatures of 0°F, then the seventh could have had a high temperature reading of 42°F.

89. **134**

$91 - 48 = 43$
$91 + 43 = 134$

The mean of 48 and 134 is 91. Each set contains the same number of data points.

90. **Julian**

Julian's three tickets must be $70, $70, and $85. His $70 ticket must be in the middle by order, and the total must be $225; this is the only possibility. Elizabeth's three tickets must be $65, $80, and $80. Her $80 tickets must be in the middle by order, and the total must also be $225; again, this is the only possibility.

91. **77**

$87 - 2 = 85$, new mean score
$85 \times 5 = 425$, new point total

Old mean score was 87 on 4 tests, so $87 \times 4 = 348$ old total points

$425 - 348 = 77$

92. $\frac{5}{12}$

The first digit has 5 chances in 9 of being odd, since 0 is not possible in the thousands place. The other three digits each have 1 chance in 2 of being odd.

$\frac{5}{9} \times \frac{1}{2} \times \frac{1}{2} \times \frac{1}{2} = \frac{5}{72}$

93. **Hamlet, because he'll win 8 out of 15 times**

There are 5 slips with numbers divisible by 3 (3, 6, 9, 12, 15) and 3 slips with numbers divisible by 4 (4, 8, 12). However, 1 of those numbers, 12, is divisible by both. Therefore, there are only 7

193

winning numbers for Othello, which leaves 8 winning numbers for Hamlet.

94. 8 pens

If you pull out 7 pens, you could have pulled all the black and all the red pens (4 + 3). To ensure that you get at least 1 blue pen, you must pull out 1 more, for a total of 8 pens.

95. $\frac{5}{12}$

$\frac{1}{3} + \frac{1}{4} = \frac{7}{12}$ of the socks are black or brown

$\frac{12}{12} - \frac{7}{12} = \frac{5}{12}$ of the socks are white

96. 8 marbles

$\frac{1}{6} = \frac{x}{48}$

$6x = 48$

$x = \frac{48}{6} = 8$

97. $\frac{18}{36} = \frac{1}{2}$

$21 - 3 = 18$ string players left
$39 - 3 = 36$ students left

$\frac{18}{36} = \frac{1}{2}$

98. 9

If there is 1 chance in 5 of pulling a plum bag, then there are 2 chances in 5 for getting a red apple bag and 2 chances in 5 of pulling a pear bag. A 2 in 5 chance is double a 1 in 5 chance, and half of 18 = 9.

99. $\frac{4}{9}$

The chances of getting a number less than 5 on one die

are $\frac{4}{6} = \frac{2}{3}$. The chances of doing so on both dice are

$\frac{2}{3} \times \frac{2}{3} = \frac{4}{9}$.

100. $\frac{1}{12}$

$\frac{1}{6} \times \frac{1}{2} = \frac{1}{12}$

101. 1

Every spread includes an even number and an odd number. When multiplied, an even and an odd number always produce an even product. When added, they produce an odd sum.

102. Maddy, Sabrina, Garrett

Garrett: $\frac{2}{7} = \frac{4}{14}$, which is less than Sabrina's $\frac{4}{13}$

If Maddy hit one bull's-eye in her next five shots, she would match Sabrina's percentage. $\frac{1}{5}$ is clearly less than her current $\frac{3}{8}$, so she ranks above Sabrina.

103. **10 units**

$6 - (-2) = 8$
$5 - (-1) = 6$

Using the Pythagorean Theorem, $8^2 + 6^2 = 64 + 36 = 100$

$\sqrt{100} = 10$

104. **2 inches**

The sides of the square are $\sqrt{2}$. The square of the hypotenuse is $(\sqrt{2})^2 + (\sqrt{2})^2 = 2 + 2 = 4$. The hypotenuse is $\sqrt{4} = 2$.

105. **3014 feet**

$8 = r$
$2(\text{pi})(8) = (16)(3.14) = $
50.24 feet around the circle in a full minute
$50.24 \times 60 = 3014.4$ feet in an hour

106. **1080**

Continuing the pattern, add 180 for each succeeding side: hexagon = 720 degrees, heptagon = 900 degrees, octagon = 1080 degrees.

107. **106 square units**

The side of the square is given by the length of the line connecting the vertices (5, 0) and (0, 9), which is the square root of $5^2 + 9^2 = 25 + 81 = 106$.

To find the area of the square, multiply $(\sqrt{106})$ by itself to get 106.

108. **Each piece is 4 inches.**

$2(l + s) = 32$, so $l + s = 16$
$ls = 48$

Only 12 and 4 add up to 16 and have a product of 48.

109. **48 centimeters**

$\frac{1}{2}$ of 128 = 64, so each square is 64 square centimeters. The side of each square is 8 centimeters.

The rectangle has two sides of 8 centimeters and two sides of 16 centimeters.

$(2 \times 16) + (2 \times 8) = 32 + 16 = 48$

195

110. **3**

Perpendicular lines have slopes that, when multiplied together, equal -1 (except in the case of slopes that are 0 and undefined).

$-\frac{1}{3} \times 3 = -1$

111. **12 hours**

$\$6.50x + \$34 = \$112$
$\$6.50x = \$78$
$x = \frac{\$78}{\$6.50} = 12$

112. **$15.75**

$\$226.25 + \$10 = \$236.25$
$\frac{\$236.25}{15} = \$15.75$

113. **13 medications**

$\$15x + \$25y = \$355$
$x + y = 15$, so $x = 15 - y$
$\$15(15 - y) + \$25y = \$355$
$\$225 - \$15y + \$25y = \$355$
$\$10y = \$130$
$y = 13$

114. **$5.00 per pound**

20 ounces = 1.25 pounds
$\frac{\$6.25}{1.25} = \$5$

115. **26 minutes**

$\$2.50 + \$0.35x = \$9.85$
$\$0.35x = \$7.35$
$x = \frac{\$7.35}{\$0.35} = 21$, the number of additional minutes after the first five
$21 + 5 = 26$ total minutes

116. **32 students**

The original ratio is 3 sophomores to every 5 juniors, so $\frac{3}{5}j = s$. The new ratio is 1 sophomore to every 2 juniors, so $j + 2 = 2(s - 1)$.

By substitution, $j + 2 = 2(\frac{3}{5}j - 1)$
$j + 2 = \frac{6}{5}j - 2$
$4 = \frac{1}{5}j$
$j = 20$
$\frac{3}{5} \times 20 = \frac{60}{5} = 12$, so $s = 12$
$20 + 12 = 32$

117. **102 containers**

$\$2.95x = \$300.90$
$\frac{\$300.90}{\$2.95} = 102$

118. **3 more cans of tomato soup**

$0.45x + 0.4(23 - x) = 9.70$
$0.45x + 9.2 - 0.4x = 9.7$
$0.05x = 0.5$

196

$x = 10$
10 cans of mushroom soup,
13 cans of tomato soup
$13 - 10 = 3$

119. $4.50

$$\$0.09 \times 104 + x = \$13.86$$
$$\$9.36 + x = \$13.86$$
$$x = \$13.86 - \$9.36 = \$4.50$$

120. 10 washers

Every group of four washers she buys will include three large and one small.

Three large washers = 21 cents
One small washer = 5 cents
The four together cost
$21 + 5 = 26$ cents.
$26x = \$2.60$
$x = 10$

She can buy 10 groups of washers, each of which includes one small washer.

121. 23 men

$$m + 41 = w$$
$$m + w = 87$$
$$m + m + 41 = 87$$
$$m + 41 + m = 87$$
$$2m = 46$$
$$m = 23$$

122. $4n - 15$

$$n + (n - 5) + 2(n - 5) =$$
$$n + n - 5 + 2n - 10 =$$
$$4n - 15$$

123. 12 children

PPP: $30 \times 4 = \$120$ plus surcharges
BBB: $35 \times 4 = \$140$ plus

surcharges
$$\$120 + \$10x = \$140 = \$5x,$$
where x equals the number of guests above eight
$$\$5x = \$20$$
$$x = 4$$
4 more than 8 is 12.

124. Dave

$$4m - 21 = m + 3$$
$$3m = 24$$
$$m = 8$$

Therefore, Audra owns 8, Bill owns 10, Chandra owns 11, and Dave owns 12.

125. 20 children

The cost for 31 tickets at the group rate would be
$31 \times \$6 = \$186$.

$8a + \$5c > \$186$
$a + c = 31$, so $c = 31 - a$
$8a + \$5(31 - a) > \$186$
$8a + \$155 - \$5a > \$186$
$3a > \$31$
$a > 10.33$

Therefore, $a = 11$ or greater, so $c = 20$ or less.

126. *D = 22h + 36*

$22 every hour = \$22h$

The materials fee of $36 must be added on, so $22h + \$36$.

127. **29**

$n + 25 < 2n - 3$
$25 < n - 3$
$28 < n$, so 29 or greater will mean that Saad read more pages.

128. **$203.75**

$\frac{\$257.50}{2} = \$128.75$

$128.75 + \$10 = \$138.75$

$138.75 + \$257.50 = \$396.25$

If the mean is $200, then the total cost of the three tickets is $600.

$600 - \$396.25 = \$203.75$, which is the median

129. **32**

The mean of e and f is 20, because $\frac{40}{2} = 20$.

$\frac{52 + 24 + 20}{3} = \frac{96}{3} = 32$

130. **Neither side: the house numbers of both streets are equal.**

$\frac{1 + 3 + 5 + 7 + 9 + 11 + 13 + 15 + 17 + 19}{10} =$

$\frac{100}{10} = 10$, the mean of the west side

$\frac{2 + 4 + 6 + 8 + 10 + 12 + 14 + 16 + 18}{9} =$

$\frac{90}{9} = 10$, the mean of the east side

131. **63**

The mode is 58 and the median is 62, so the youngest two are 58. The second oldest must be 66, because 62 is halfway between 58 and 66. The friends are 58, 58, 66, and 70, which totals to 252, and $\frac{252}{4} = 63$.

132. **5**

$2 + 5 + a = 4 + 8 + b$
$7 + a = 12 + b$
$a = 5 + b$

133. **75**

Monday = 70
Friday = 75
Thursday = 80
Wednesday = 75
Tuesday = $\frac{75 + 75}{2}$ = 75

There are three 75s and no other recurring figures, so 75 is the mode.

134. **32.5**

$3.25 \times 10 = 32.5$

135. **greatest = 21, least = 17**

If the other half of the students all write poems that are 24 lines long, the median will be $\frac{24 + 18}{2}$ = 21, or the greatest possible figure. Alternatively, if the other half all write poems

that are 16 lines long, the median will be $\frac{18 + 16}{2}$ = 17, or the least possible figure.

136. **$g(x)$, for x = 1; $g(x)$, for x > 3; $g(x)$, for x < 0**

$1^3 = 1$ and $3^1 = 3$, so $g(x)$ is greater for $x = 1$.
3^x increases more quickly than x^3 for $x > 3$ (at 3, the two functions are equal).
For a negative x, $f(x)$ is negative, $g(x)$ positive though fractional, so $g(x)$ is greater.

137. **2 inches**

$4^3 = (2^2)^3 = 2^6$
$\frac{2^7}{2^6} = 2$

138. **Any value such that 0 < x < 1**

Multiplying numbers between 0 and 1 by themselves creates progressively smaller numbers that approach but do not actually reach 0. Some examples: $x = \frac{1}{2}$, $\left(\frac{1}{2}\right)^5 = \frac{1}{32}$, and $\left(\frac{1}{2}\right)^6 = \frac{1}{64}$

139. **$n + 1$**

The factors are m^0, or 1; m^1, or m; m^2, m^3, ... m^n. Therefore, the answer is $n + 1$.

140. **At (0, 0) and (1, 1)**

$0^2 = 0$ $0^3 = 0$
$1^2 = 1$ $1^3 = 1$

141. **81 names**

$9^4 = (3^2)^4 = 3^8$
$\frac{3^8}{3^4} = 3^{(8-4)} = 3^4 = 81$

142. 0.5 ounces

$3x + a = 5$, where x is the weight of an individual disk and a is the weight of the container

$11x + a = 9$
$a = 5 - 3x$ and $a = 9 - 11x$
$5 - 3x = 9 - 11x$
$8x = 4$
$x = 0.5$

143. 2:30 P.M.

$\frac{5}{12} = \frac{2.5}{6}$, so 2.5 hours after he began
Noon + 2.5 hours = 2:30

144. 10:01 A.M.

$-12 + 4m = 52$
$4m = 64$
$m = \frac{64}{4} = 16$
9:45 A.M. + 16 minutes = 10:01 A.M.

145. 2 kilograms

$35 - 24 = 11$, so the 5 metal plates removed from the box weigh a total of 11 kilograms.

$\frac{11}{5} = 2.2$ kilograms each
$15 \times 2.2 = 33$, so the 15 metal plates originally packed in the box weigh 33 kilograms.
$35 - 33 = 2$ kilograms, which is the weight of the box.

146. 27 times

On Friday, it is x units
Saturday, $3x$
Sunday, $3(3x) = 9x$
Monday, $3(9x) = 27x$

147. 16 miles per hour

The truck goes 140 miles in 2.5 hours.

$\frac{140}{2.5} = 56$ miles per hour
3:30 + 1 hour = 4:30, so 140 miles in 3.5 hours

$\frac{140}{3.5} = 40$ miles per hour
56 miles per hour − 40 miles per hour = 16 miles per hour

148. $t = h - nc$

nc = total height of the stack of cubes
$t + nc = h$, so $t = h - nc$

149. 29.4 miles

She spends 10.5 hours swimming with the current, so $10.5 \times 1.6 = 16.8$ miles with the current. She spends 10.5 hours swimming against the current, so $10.5 \times 1.2 = 12.6$ miles against the current.

$16.8 + 12.6 = 29.4$ miles

150. 12 questions every day

There are 31 days in both July and August, so he has a total of 62 days. $\frac{496}{62} = 8$, so he needs to write 8 questions a day. If he wrote only half the questions he needs to write in July, he needs to write an extra 4 questions a day in August, so $8 + 4 = 12$.

151. 4,970

$210 - 69 = 141$

The only possible combination of two integers greater than 69 that sums to 141 is 70 and 71.

$70 \times 71 = 4{,}970$

152. 24 years old

25 and 49 are the only square numbers for which the smaller number times 2 is 1 greater than the greater number.

153. Green at 2:10 P.M., then yellow at 2:11 P.M.

The cycle lasts 45 seconds. Three minutes = 4×45 seconds, so in 3 minutes, or at 2:10, green will repeat. The next cycle takes 45 seconds, followed by 15 seconds of green to round out the full

minute. At 2:11, the light will just be turning yellow.

154. 10 laps

Let a be the number of laps.

$a + a + 1 + a + 2 + a + 3 + a + 4 + a + 5 + a + 6 \geq 90$
$7a + 21 \geq 90$
$7a \geq 69$
$a \geq \frac{69}{7}$

$\frac{69}{7}$ is just under 10, so $a = 10$ or more.

155. 600

The closer the two integers are to each other, the greater their product will be; 24 and 25 are within 1 of each other.

$24 + 25 = 49$

$24 \times 25 = 600$

156. **5**

For the remainder to be 1 when $q + 3$ is divided by p, the remainder when $q + 2$ is divided by p must be 0. Therefore, the remainder when $q + 1$ is divided by p must be $p - 1$. Since the remainder when q is divided by p is 3, $p - 1$ must equal 4, so $p = 5$.

157. $\frac{2}{7}$

The probability of choosing a blue shirt in which to run is $\frac{2}{7}$. He chooses one shirt to wear, so there are six shirts remaining in the drawer. Therefore, the probability of

choosing a white shirt after the shower is $\frac{4}{6}$, or $\frac{2}{3}$.

$\frac{2}{7} \times \frac{2}{3} = \frac{6}{21} = \frac{2}{7}$

158. **0**

If six students receive the correct note, then the seventh student must also receive the correct note.

159. $\frac{1}{4}$

Anything times an even number produces an even number. The only possibility that gives an odd product is if both Eva and Jessie roll an odd number. That will happen $\frac{1}{2} \times \frac{1}{2} = \frac{1}{4}$ of the time.

160. $\frac{1}{6}$

$\frac{1}{3} \times \frac{1}{2} \times \frac{1}{1} = \frac{1}{6}$

161. $\frac{2}{7-s}$

There are two red sleeping bags that she can pick. There are $(7 - s)$ remaining sleeping bags in the back of the car.

162. **6**

$\frac{3}{4}$ of $24 = 18$
$24 - 18 = 6$

163. $\frac{5}{12}$

There's a $\frac{6}{9} = \frac{2}{3}$ chance that the first can will be diet and a $\frac{5}{8}$ probability that the second one will be diet as well (there are 5 diet cans remaining and 8 in all).

$\frac{2}{3} \times \frac{5}{8} = \frac{10}{24} = \frac{5}{12}$

164. 400 orders

$\frac{64}{100} = \frac{x}{625}$

$64 \times 625 = 100x$

$40,000 = 100x$

$400 = x$

165. $600,000

$\$475,000 + \$95,000 = \$570,000$

$0.95x = \$570,000$

$x = \frac{\$570,000}{0.95} = \$600,000$

166. 15 pints

$\frac{3}{10}$ are vanilla, and $\frac{3}{10} = \frac{x}{50}$

$10x = 150$

$x = 15$

167. 77 members

$239 - 5 = 234$, so there are 234 total members of the Oppressive and Domineering Parties. A ratio of 9:4 means that $\frac{9}{13}$ of these 234 are Oppressive Party members, so $\frac{9}{13} = \frac{x}{234}$.

$9 \times 234 = 13x$

$2106 = 13x$

$\frac{2106}{13} = 162 = x$

If there are 162 Oppressive Party members, then there are $239 - 162 = 77$ members who are not part of the Oppressive Party.

168. 200 students

Twenty-five percent of the students play IM soccer, IM volleyball, or both. The totals for the two IM sports add to 29%, so 4% of students play both IM soccer and IM volleyball.

4% of students = 8

$\frac{4}{100} = \frac{8}{x}$

$4x = 800$

$x = 200$

169. 27 games

They had 3 wins when they scored 2 goals or fewer, so

$\frac{8}{x} = \frac{15}{100}$

$300 = 15x$

$x = 20$

As the problem states, they scored at least 3 goals twice as often as they scored 2 goals or 1 goal.

$20 \times 2 = 40$ games in which they scored at least 3 goals

$40 \times 0.6 = 24$ games in which

they scored 3 or more goals
24 + 3 = 27, so they won 27
games.

170. 36 yellow tulips

$\frac{x}{24 + x} = 0.6$

$x = 0.6(24 + x) = 14.4 + 0.6x$

$0.4x = 14.4$

$x = \frac{14.4}{0.4} = 36$

171. 7 seniors

35% + 25% + 15% = 75%
5 players = 25%, so 1 player =
5%
7 × 5% = 35%, so 7 players are
seniors

172. $36; $7.20

48 × $0.75 = $36
4 × $7.20 = $28.80
$36 − $28.80 = $7.20

204

173. 200 cubic feet

30 feet × 16 feet = 480 square
feet for the playground
480 square feet × $\frac{5}{12}$ feet = $\frac{480}{12}$ ×
5 = 40 × 5 = 200 cubic feet

174. 9 hours

$\frac{172}{6} = 62$, so his rate is 62 miles
per hour

372 − 93 = 279, so the total
distance is 2 × 279 = 558 miles

$\frac{558 \text{ miles}}{62 \text{ miles per hour}} = 9$, so the trip
takes 9 hours

175. 5:48 A.M.

$\frac{1}{3}$ hour = 20 minutes

$\frac{1}{4}$ hour = 15 minutes

$\frac{1}{5}$ hour = 12 minutes

$\frac{1}{6}$ hour = 10 minutes

20 + 15 + 12 + 10 = 57 minutes
6:45 A.M. − 57 minutes = 5:48 A.M.

176. 12 times

There are 8 pints in a gallon.

96 pints ÷ $\frac{8 \text{ pints}}{\text{gallon}} = 12$

177. $2.80

Each friend buys $\frac{40}{5} = 8$
packages.
Each package at the bulk rate
costs $\frac{\$19}{10} = \$1.90$.
$2.25 − $1.90 = $0.35 savings
per package
8 × $0.35 = $2.80

178. 16 meters by 3 meters

16 × 3 = 48

16 + 16 + 3 + 3 = 38

179. $\frac{3}{p}$ **yards**

1 yard = 36 inches, so the board is 3 yards long. Each piece is $\frac{3}{p}$ yards long.

180. **Exactly 2 hours**

The mean of the two movies is $\frac{1}{2}$ × (4 hours 10 minutes 20 seconds) = 2 hours 5 minutes 10 seconds. The original movie is that length + $\frac{1}{2}$ (10 minutes 20 seconds), and the sequel is that length − $\frac{1}{2}$ (10 minutes 20 seconds).

M1 = M2 + 10 minutes + 20 seconds

M1 + M2 = 4 hours + 10 minutes + 20 seconds

M2 = 2 hours